ENGLISH FARMING

GENERAL EDITOR
W. J. TURNER

✽

The Editor is most grateful to all those who have
so kindly helped in the selection of illustrations,
especially to officials of the various public
Museums, Libraries and Galleries, and
to all others who have generously
allowed pictures and MSS.
to be reproduced.

ENGLISH FARMING

SIR E. JOHN RUSSELL

INTRODUCTION
BY HENRY WILLIAMSON

WITH
12 PLATES IN COLOUR
AND
22 ILLUSTRATIONS IN
BLACK & WHITE

WILLIAM COLLINS OF LONDON
MCMXXXXII

PRODUCED BY
ADPRINT LIMITED LONDON

*

PRINTED
IN GREAT BRITAIN
BY WILLIAM BROWN AND CO. LTD. LONDON

SECOND EDITION

LIST OF ILLUSTRATIONS

PLATES IN COLOUR

PLOUGHING   SOWING   HARROWING
From the Luttrell Psalter c. 1340

BREAKING CLODS   WEEDING   REAPING
From the Luttrell Psalter c. 1340

STACKING THE SHEAVES   CARTING THE HARVEST
From the Luttrell Psalter c. 1340

LINCOLN HORSE FAIR
Oil painting by William Turner of Oxford

HAYMAKERS
Oil painting by George Stubbs, 1724-1806

REAPERS
Oil painting by George Stubbs, 1724-1806

THE STABLE INTERIOR
Oil painting by George Morland

A SOW OF THE IMPROVED BREED BELONGING TO HIS GRACE THE DUKE
OF BEDFORD
Oil painting by George Morland

MR. PAWLETT WITH HIS LEICESTER SHEEP, WINNERS AT THE FIRST ROYAL
SHOW, 1839
Oil painting by an unknown artist

HARVEST FIELDS
The Village of Stanton Harcourt in the background
Water colour by William Turner of Oxford

THE HARVEST
Oil painting by James Bateman

THE RED OX   THE BLACK SOW
Tempera paintings by John Armstrong

BLACK & WHITE ILLUSTRATIONS

SHORT BIBLIOGRAPHY

British Agriculture : the Principles of Future Policy
   By Lord Astor and B. S. Rowntree. Longmans,
   1938

English Farming, Past and Present
   By Lord Ernle. Longmans, 1936

Pilgrimage of British Farming
   By A. D. Hall. Murray, 1913

British Breeds of Livestock
   Ministry of Agriculture Bulletin No. 86. Stationery
   Office

The Farm and the Nation
   By E. J. Russell. Allen & Unwin, 1933

A Student's Book on Soils and Manures
   By E. J. Russell. Cambridge University Press,
   1940

The Land, Now and To-morrow
   By R. G. Stapledon. Faber & Faber, 1935

Foundations of Agricultural Economics
   By J. A. Venn. Cambridge University Press, 1933

Agriculture : the Science and Practice of British Farming
   By J. A. S. Watson and J. A. More. Oliver &
   Boyd, Edinburgh, 1937

THE GOLDEN VALLEY
Drawing in colour by Samuel Palmer

INTRODUCTION

IF anyone had told me five years ago that I should be a farmer in Norfolk during the second phase of the Great War, I should not have believed him. Yet my determination to become a farmer, at the age of forty years, was perhaps not so sudden or unpremeditated as at the time I imagined.

Five years ago, in 1936, as I sat by my open hearth in a Devon cottage, while the salmon river outside roared in spate, bringing down roots and trees from the valley which ended as a hillside cut on the wild moor, I realised definitely that I needed new stimulation as an artist. I mused on the orange groves of Florida ; the great silver salmon of Newfoundland ; the mountains of the Tyrol or the Black Forest, or perhaps Corsica ; of the luxuriant forests of New Zealand, with its vision of strange mountains and rainbow trout in the rivers.

7

I felt I had outlived my Devon countryside, with its otters, foxes, stags, salmon, and badgers. I had written books about these things, also about the village and the people. There was nothing more to write ; I had used up all my knowledge.

My four sons were entered for Blundells School ; in due course they would go there, and be fitted for some sort of future. What future, I did not know ; I had no thoughts, no ideas, about it.

The young men of Britain would have to make their own future. They were Britain ; and they would make a new Britain, I hoped, better than the one which I and the friends of my youth had known. We had known what it was to kill, and be killed, about the time we had learned to shave. Afterwards, we walked the streets seeking work ; while the Old Men pooh-pooh'd our ideas of a better country. The dole queues remained, and the world did not seem to be getting any better, despite the universal platitudes. Indeed, it seemed to many that the platitudes were a semi-unconscious smoke-screen put up to hide reality. A world different from that which broke periodically into war needed fundamental changes ; not platitudes.

And so time went on, until five years ago I decided suddenly to do my own small active part in the rebuilding of a better Britain. Farming was in a bad way ; so I would start to farm. Many labourers' cottages were rotten ; I would rebuild as many as I could. By chance I saw a near-derelict farm in Norfolk, and bought it six months later. I bought it against the advice of lawyers, land valuers, relatives, friends and acquaintances. An experienced farmer told me that English land had not been so cheap for a hundred and fifty years. The near-destitution of so much of the English arable farming was a symptom of the decay of the Old World ; but I knew the true English spirit, and believed it was due for a great revival. In that revival, I believed, English land, the mother of the race, and the English people themselves, would be put first.

So I started farming, and in an old lorry took my belongings and part of the family (the others to follow) across England, from the lush West Country, with its rains and rocky streams and soft airs and burring speech, to hardy East Anglia, with its droughts and sluggish rivers and sharp, keen air and shrill, clipped speech. I could not have had such a contrast if I had gone to California or the Rockies—and I was in the best land of all, England !

As I look back now, with the fourth year of my farming venture nearing completion, I am not sorry I turned farmer. People told me I had undertaken a tough job, and I knew it ; but I did not know how tough it would turn out. I've had to buy my experience, in everything. Those three condemned cottages, which I rebuilt myself, are finished now ; but it took a long time, while farm-

8

PLOUGHING   SOWING   HARROWING

From the Luttrell Psalter c. 1340

Cantate domino + benedicite no
mini eius: annunciate de die in die

Afferte domino patrie gencium af
ferte domino gloriam + honorem:

gaudebunt campi + omnia que in
eis sunt

BREAKING CLODS   WEEDING   REAPING

From the Luttrell Psalter c. 1340

work was neglected. When they were done, I had to rebuild and alter two others for a farmhouse; for there was none with the land. The family, five children with father and mother, lived for months in a broken-roofed granary with no windows and a wet brick floor, with only a small stove and no water or bath or drains. The farm was weedy, hedges tall and ragged, gates broken or fallen, the roads were bogs or deep ruts, the buildings ruinous and rat-ridden, the meadows snipe-bogs, the woods full of broken trees and dead elderberries. And all this viewed daily, hourly, by an impatient, imaginative temperament, which longed to see it altered in a moment, but which, to make the transformation real, had to earn money by writing articles, often half the night.

I am glad I undertook the work. Our bullocks lost money (beef didn't pay), the sheep trade fell and flockmasters sold up, wheat was subsidised, and then, at our first harvest, the barley trade (East Anglia grows the finest malting barley) crashed. But I had foreseen a greater decline; and although it meant that my capital was gone and an overdraft was mounting up, I knew things would come right.

They came right when the war broke out. Immediately the Government set about putting things on a proper basis. We farmers now have stable markets. We know what we will get for our pigs, our milk, our sugar-beet, our beef, our mutton. We can plough, cultivate and drill for a crop of barley knowing that we will not get only the bare costs of production back after threshing and taking samples of corn to the merchants at their stands in the Corn Hall, but an increase enabling us to farm better the following season.

My friends and advisers, who thought me rash, even foolhardy, to buy land in 1936, now congratulate me on my foresight. The weeds on the land are gone, the meadows are being drained (Government grant covers half the cost), the arable fields are being chalked (to sweeten the soil, again a half-cost grant), the roads are made up (oh, the blisters of 1937 digging 1,000 tons of flints and gravel out of a pit!), my home-bred bullocks are in the yards, treading clean barley straw to make the dung to grow the corn and the sugar-beet of next season. Sheep graze the grassy hills; the circular saw, driven by the tractor, cuts up tons of firewood from the reclaimed hedges. My three sons go to the village school, while the eldest, aged 14, drives the tractor and ploughs the fields. Their mother looks after the hens, and mends the clothes, while a village maid cleans our small renovated farmhouse and cooks with electricity.

Norfolk is famous for its wild pheasants. Pigeons come from Scandinavia to the woods, and once a week the villagers, by invitation, shoot them from hides in the woods. Wild duck flight to the willow-fringed pond on the meadows, geese pass over, woodcock flap across the North Sea and settle in the hedge-bottoms, trout rise in the chalk-stream which runs through the lower land ; so we do not lack for food. Our mill in the chaff-barn grinds barley and wheat for flour, for a variety of loaves we bake ourselves. And, of course, we have our own milk and cream and butter. And lest this seem too selfish a catalogue, I must add that not the least of our achievements is giving employment to four families and a home to three others in warm, dry cottages. Those four years gave me some white hairs (the placid temperament is the best for a farmer's life, with its myriad anxieties !), but I do not regret anything. All was, and is, experience.

It has taken a war to put British farming on its feet, and to bring back to us generally the idea that work is the true basis of life in the world. A nation that neglects its land, and its peasants—which are its root-stock—will perish. The idea of living by easy money is no good. Napoleon said that toil produced a hard and virile race, while trade produced a soft and crafty people ; and that is true. We British are hard and virile, and we must have overseas trade in order to build up a high standard of life ; but the cut-price, get-rich-quick idiom was beginning to spoil that hardness and virility. The by-products of that past epoch were over-intellectualism, spiciness and hyper-stimulation of feeling : too many cocktails, too-glamorous movies, a rootlessness showing itself in artistic distortion ; pavementism. These things were an emanation of the same system that produced the dole-queues, slums, malnutrition, the " class-war." The war has brought us back to the fundamentals of life ; and when it is over, on the basis of our new, hard economy, we shall build a fine civilisation in this country, and its Empire, on the simple virtues of life. There will be enough work for everyone under a modernised, planned system which puts first its land and its people.

I want to see town children educated by bodywork in the country, getting to know its trees, its birds, its coasts, its soils, mountains, streams, counties. I want to see country children having technical education ; I want to see them travelling to the Empire, and returning with a knowledge of what their inheritance truly means. I want to see thistles and docks as rare plants in Kew Gardens— extinct elsewhere ! I desire to see gardens where once there were slums ; to see salmon leaping again by London Bridge, in water no longer polluted by sewers, chemical plant, and all the filthy, chaotic dribble of an unplanned, many-headed commercial monster which in the past put profit first and regarded human life as a mere accessory. These and all the other things of a full and proper social life are not only possible, but inevitable ; they will arise from the purgatory of the present.

HENRY WILLIAMSON

A COTSWOLD FARM
Oil painting by Gilbert Spencer

FEW classes of the community have received more well-meaning advice or have shown less resentment about it than the farmers. Before the war, travellers landing at Liverpool and passing through the grass region to Euston found few animals and much neglect ; motorists detected straggling hedges and land going out of cultivation. · And if the traveller were fortunate enough to meet the farmer he would probably have learned that this was a bad season ; corn might look well but grass was very poor (or *vice versa*), and in any case selling prices were low and costs high. If he was still more fortunate and was invited into the house he would have found standards of hospitality and of comfort that would have reconciled him to the evils of the present and the fears for the future.

Farmers have learned by long experience that trouble may come at any time, and that nothing can be deemed safe till it is sold and paid for. They have gradually evolved systems of farming having wide insurance value :

part of the scheme may come out well in a dry year, but another part does better in a wet year. Since the year cannot be both wet and dry, some of their labour is always liable to be lost, and this naturally is in their minds when they are summing up the prospects for the season.

In the short space available it is manifestly impossible to write a full account of British agriculture, nor is it necessary since the excellent textbook of Scott Watson and More already provides this. Nor did I wish to give a few sketches, pleasant though the task would be, especially if one could write in lyrical vein ; this has been done many times, among others by A. G. Street, a farmer who fortunately discovered his gift for writing ; by Fred Kitchen, a farm worker ; by Adrian Bell, Henry Williamson and others.

Instead I have endeavoured to present a concise account of the results of English farming : setting out what it is actually accomplishing ; and I must ask the reader to remember that the British farmer is neither a gardener paid to keep the landscape tidy, nor a public servant paid to till the Nation's land, but a plain man seeking to get his living, recognising his responsibility to his staff of workers and to his farm, and anxious to do his best by both of them. Like the rest of the community he is bound by the laws of economics and is often driven to action or inaction that he regrets. The fact that he has survived the critical years between 1921 and 1938 shows that his methods have merit ; but they have done more than ensure survival : they have led to a high output per worker and per acre, and have given workers better hours, easier conditions and better remuneration than in most of the Continental countries. Better still, constant improvement is sought, and it is now more and more recognised that a prosperous agriculture forms the only sound basis for a prosperous national life.

1

THE PLAN OF THE FARM AND THE FARMING PROGRAMME.

DURING war the importance of British agriculture is widely recognised, but few people realise that even in peace-time agriculture is one of our largest industries. It employs directly about a million people, in addition to the large number needed to supply materials. Farm land and rough grazing between them occupy more than three-quarters of our island, and in spite of their apparent immensity the cities, towns, villages, roads, railways, houses and gardens everywhere cover only about one-tenth of its total area—no more indeed than is occupied by deer forests and woodlands.

STACKING THE SHEAVES   CARTING THE HARVEST

From the Luttrell Psalter c. 1340

LINCOLN HORSE FAIR

Oil painting by William Turner of Oxford

English agriculture differs fundamentally from commerce and industries. It deals very largely with living things—animals and plants that can never be left alone for long ; farmers and the leading workers must therefore reside on the spot and be ready at any hour and every day to give such attention as is necessary. Farming thus becomes not simply their livelihood but their mode of life. Both animals and plants are largely dependent on the weather, and as this cannot be forecasted with any certainty it is impossible to keep to any rigid programme of operations. The work of the day must be settled on the day itself and on the spot ; everything later can be provisional only and subject to the condition : weather permitting. This habit of making daily decisions engenders a spirit of independence of mind and judgment often mistaken by superficial observers for obstinacy.

The soil and the situation of the farms determine what crops can and what cannot be grown economically, and so determine the farming system, but there is no sure way of finding these out except by trial—and trial always implies a certain proportion of failures. Like other business people, farmers can undertake only limited risks and are therefore often precluded from adopting new methods until they know fairly accurately the chances of success. Moreover, the fundamental processes of farming are governed by Nature's laws and not by our own : seed time and harvest, the period needed to produce an animal, the age at which a cow can begin to give milk—these and many other things which set the pace of farming operations are out of our control. The unit of time is not the day or the week, but the year ; sometimes indeed it is longer, and covers the whole period of the rotation. Farming therefore cannot be changed rapidly, and a system once adopted can only slowly be altered : this has often caused farmers to be wrongly regarded as very conservative and unwilling to change their so-called old-fashioned ways.

These special characteristics of farming make it unsuitable for the operation of the great joint stock enterprises, and, excepting for a few family organisations, farming by companies is practically unknown in Great Britain. Instead there is a kind of triple association of landowner, farmer and farm worker. In its simplest form the landowner provides at a very low rate of interest the permanent capital items : the buildings, farm roads, drains, etc. ; he is expected to foster the improvement of live-stock and to try new methods of cultivation, varieties of crops or systems of farming likely to be helpful on his estate. The farmer provides the working capital items—the animals, implements, seeds, manures, etc.—but within the range (usually very wide) of the covenant with the landowner is free to crop how he pleases, though certain weeds and plant and animal diseases are not tolerated. The worker is much more personally concerned in the whole business than in a factory ; he is often of ancient stock and the most permanent member of the association ; in a quiet way he has considerable voice in the management both of the land and the animals :

"For, whoever pays the taxes, old Muss' Hobden owns the land."

Labour troubles are almost unknown ; wages are regulated by Wages Boards composed of equal numbers of farmers and workers, and three impartial members acceptable to both sides and appointed by the Minister of Agriculture. These boards have usually worked smoothly and effectively, thanks to a good choice of members and the sense of responsibility of all parties, including the great unions concerned, and there has been a steady improvement in the conditions of life of the farm worker which, it is hoped, will continue.

A large part of the land of England and Wales is in farms ranging about 100 to 200 acres, but the size varies, according to the natural conditions, from 600 or 700 acres in the rolling open country of the East and South to some 50 acres in the hill farms of the North and West. The determining factor is always the area that one man can adequately supervise. The large farms carry a large paid staff ; the smaller ones are commonly run by the family, much quiet, efficient work being done by its women and children. The still smaller holdings, below 50 acres, often praised by writers, are not liked by those who work them, and their number steadily decreases.

HOLDINGS OF LAND IN ENGLAND AND WALES 1930 AND 1938

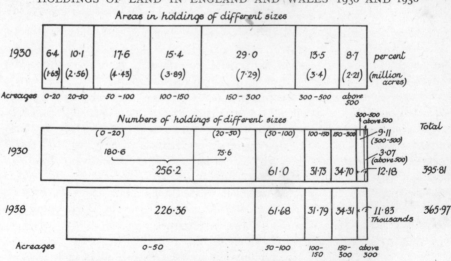

The wide variations in conditions in different parts of the country necessitate corresponding variations in the agriculture ; but there have always

DRAY HORSES, BELONGING TO HENRY MEUX, ESQ.
Coloured engraving by T. Fairland after A. Cooper, c. 1830

been certain underlying common features. From medieval times up to the end of the eighteenth century a three-course rotation was widely followed : first a winter corn crop, wheat, oats or rye ; then spring corn, oats, barley, peas or beans ; and then the land was left uncropped for a year, during which time the animals could graze on whatever wild vegetation sprang up. This system was both ancient and widespread, but it was not very productive. It gave little food for animals during the winter, and so there had to be much slaughtering and salting down in late autumn when the grass gave out. This led to a temporary period of feasting that still survives in our " fairs," " feasts " and " wakes " ; but the winter that followed was long and dreary, and the yearning for the spring must have been very intense. This, too, has survived, for it inspired some of our finest literature.

This old system was profoundly modified in 'the eighteenth and early nineteenth centuries, when the fallows were replaced by root crops : turnips, swedish turnips, mangolds and potatoes ; and clover and various grasses, usually spoken of as "seeds" or "ley" crops, were inserted between the winter and the spring corn crop. Thus arose the famous four-course or Norfolk rotation : first roots, then barley, then clover sown in the barley but not adversely affected by it, and then wheat, after which the rotation began again. Half the arable land was thus in grain crops suited to human consumption and half in fodder crops for live stock. Part of the farm was also in grass which also furnished food for animals. The effect of the rotation on the life of the country was far-reaching. The additional animal food meant a larger animal population and therefore more meat, milk, bacon and eggs ; further, the animals could be fed during winter, and it was not necessary to slaughter them in autumn. Fresh meat became available all the year round, and a great Christmas show of fat stock started by the Smithfield Club in 1799 proved what the new methods could do. The animals during winter made large quantities of farmyard manure, so that larger crops could be grown, and these fed more animals, giving still more manure and still larger crops. It was a period of optimism, and the nineteenth century agriculturists thought, like many others, in terms of ascending spirals, of progress onwards and upwards for ever.

During three-quarters of the nineteenth century this rotation proved admirably suited to British conditions, and it was developed to a high standard of technical efficiency. It required a considerable amount of labour at a weekly wage not exceeding the price of four bushels (about 250 lb.) of wheat, and so long as this was available it worked well. But from about 1880 onwards the opening up of the North American prairies led to the production of quantities of wheat which was sold here at prices far below those at which our farmers could produce it. Public opinion was entirely against the imposition of any tariff on food, and farmers both on the prairies and at home were left to solve the problem as best they could. The prairie farmers suffered and had to accept a very low standard of living and to adopt methods which led ultimately to terrible destruction of the soil. The home farmers suffered equally ; many went under, and there was great distress in the countryside.

But out of it all there emerged new kinds of farming, a recognition that the system should not be fixed but adapted to the natural conditions of the farm and to the available markets. As the conditions are very variable, so the methods have to be variable, and one of the great achievements of modern agriculture is that it has given the farmer a wide choice of possibilities out of which he selects those best suited to his farm and market. The Eastern Counties have remained predominantly arable, but grow sugar beet and potatoes instead of swedes, and produce more milk and less fat winter beef ; the Midlands and particularly the Western Counties have turned more to grass. Changes in public taste have been recognised and provided for. Younger and more tender meat is provided, and there is a great increase in the production of eggs and poultry. The growing demand for a more varied diet was met by increasing considerably the area under potatoes, vegetables and fruit, and above all by increasing greatly the production of milk.

Nevertheless the agriculture of the country still falls very much within the framework of the old four-course rotation, although both crops and uses are more varied. Approximately one-half of the arable land of England and Wales is still in grain, one-quarter in root crops and one-quarter in seeds leys as in the old days. Between the grassland and the arable, however, the relations are much less constant. Some land is always in grass, some is always in arable, but a considerable area is sometimes the one and sometimes the other, according to economic conditions. In periods of depression arable land is laid down to grass; in periods when high production is required, as in war-time, it is reconverted to arable. This is one of the simplest and commonest adjustments by which farmers adapt themselves to changing economic conditions. As in

UTILISATION OF LAND IN GREAT BRITAIN
Total area 56·2 million acres

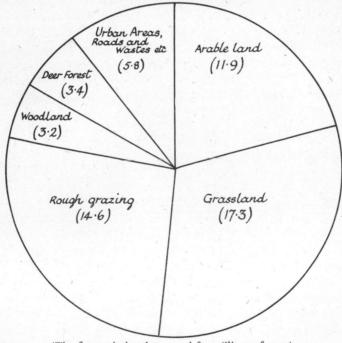

(The figures in brackets stand for millions of acres)

most other advanced countries, however, the tendency is for arable land to be converted to grass.

A second adjustment is also made at the other end of the scale. The " grass land," which is fenced and looked after, merges insensibly into " rough grazing " which is not. Some of the rough grazing always remains as such, but a good deal of it is marginal and can be converted into grassland whenever economic conditions justify. The areas of these three groups of land in England and Wales have been, in millions of acres :—

	1914	1918	1928	1938
Arable land	11·00	12·40	10·11	8·88
Permanent grassland ...	16·12	14·59	15·40	15·83
Rough grazing	3·78	3·99	5·18	5·61
Total ...	30·90	30·98	30·69	30·32

Total area of land, 37·13 million acres.

These fluctuations and adjustments do not cut deeply into the lay-out of the countryside. In many places the fields remain much as they have been for long past. On our own farm at Rothamsted most of the field boundaries of 1936 are almost identical with those of 1623, and many of the old names still survive. Oaks planted during the Napoleonic wars to help in repelling future would-be invaders have been felled in this war, but in general hedges and trees are left to shelter the animals, and as they grow slowly no avoidable disturbance is undertaken. The roots of English agriculture, like those of English country life, go deep into the past, and no one can fully understand either without a knowledge of its history.

II

THE LIVE-STOCK OF GREAT BRITAIN

THERE had always been many varieties of domestic animals in Great Britain, but the first successful efforts at improvement were made in the second half of the eighteenth century by Robert Bakewell, of Dishley, Leicestershire, a farmer with real genius for live-stock. Up to his time animals that fattened well were sent early to the butcher, while those that did not were kept for breeding. He realised that this was wrong, and sought deliberately to produce animals that fattened easily and economically. In this he was very successful, and by careful in-breeding he fixed his types.

ROBERT BAKEWELL, 1725–1795
Engraving by F. Engelheart, 1842

His Leicester sheep gave rise to our most popular breed of sheep, and though his Longhorn cattle did not survive, his methods practised by his pupil Charles Colling produced the Shorthorn, now our most popular breed of cattle. His animals fetched high prices ; indeed, some people complained that they were " too dear to buy and too fat to eat." But the cost of his experiments was even higher and he is said to have died poor. British agriculture, however, owes him an incalculable debt, and he gave to countless other farmers the means to live.

Charles Colling farmed at Ketton, near Darlington. After his return from Dishley he was dining with his brother Robert and a friend, who jointly wanted a bull. Charles said he had seen an excellent animal as he passed Haughtonle-Skerne church ; it had a mossy coat, looked like putting on fat and, most important from Charles' point of view, was mellow to the touch : the ordinary cattle of the time were hard as boards. It belonged to a small farmer and bricklayer, and Charles was authorised to buy it for eight guineas. But Robert did not much care for it, and after a time Charles, who still kept his faith in it, bought it back at its original price. He named it Hubback and hunted round for suitable mates, also mellow to the touch ; with the help of his wife he ultimately found four. From this small herd all our Shorthorns are descended, and Hubback rose from obscure beginnings to become the father of a famous breed. There was, of course, much in-breeding ; Comet, one of the most renowned of all domestic animals of the nineteenth century, was got by Favourite out of one of his own daughters.

Colling's main purpose was beef, but later on a milk branch of the breed was started by Thomas Bates, of Halton, in the Tyne valley, and later Kirklevington. A legacy left him by an aunt enabled him to purchase the animals he fancied and to make the necessary experiments.

Numerous other breeds of cattle, of sheep and of pigs have been developed, mostly by farmers with a genius for judging animals. The records are kept in the herd books published by the various breed societies. An animal gains entry only by birth. For Shorthorns four crosses of registered blood are required for females, and five for males ; a non-pedigree herd can thus be graded up by the use of registered bulls for four or five generations. For Aberdeen Angus the rules are stricter ; animals can be admitted only if their parents' names are already there. There is a large export of pedigree animals from Great Britain.

The ordinary farmer's live-stock is not pure, and frequently is deliberately cross-bred, but the pedigree stock is essential as the foundation. " Scrub " animals are widely condemned, though there are still many of them.

MILK PRODUCTION

For a long time this corresponded with a fairly steady consumption of 19 gallons of liquid milk per head per annum ; for two or three years before the war it was rising. The milk producer's work is hard, for the cows must be milked and tended twice a day ; the first time may be at four or five in the morning, and that for 365 days of the year. Moreover, cows are exacting animals and do not like a change of attendants. The milking machine has simplified matters, but the human touch is still necessary.

Milk production is widespread, and few counties have less than five cows in milk per 100 acres of cultivated land. The largest numbers are in Cheshire,

HAYMAKERS

Oil painting by George Stubbs, 1724-1806

REAPERS

Oil painting by George Stubbs, 1724-1806

THE DURHAM OX
Oil painting by J. Boultby

where there are no fewer than 26 per 100 acres of cultivated land ; Lancashire and Somerset are close competitors in total numbers, though less in density ; then follow the West Riding, Devon, Shropshire and Wiltshire. On the other hand, some very highly farmed regions have very few cows ; the Holland division of Lincoln has 2·5 and the Isle of Ely only 2·2 per 100 acres.

The main development of dairying has thus been in the grass counties, but not in all of them ; milk has to be carried quickly to the consumer, and so its production is limited by the transport available. In the old days this was almost entirely by rail, but nowadays huge milk lorries of 1,000 to 3,000 gallons capacity are much used. A large part of the milk is produced by small working farmers who can keep close watch on their animals. The average size of a dairy herd is about sixteen cows. But some of the finest dairy farms in the country are large : the Rayleigh farms in Essex, Mr. Hosier's in Wiltshire, and others.

The old method of building up a commercial herd was to go into the market and buy cows having well-shaped udders and prominent " milk veins " ; now there is much careful breeding for milk, the bull being chosen because of the milk yield of his offspring, and the dam because of her own performance.

The most popular dairy cow is the Shorthorn. Probably the next favourite is the Ayrshire, the only native dairy animal of Scotland ; it originated in the eighteenth century in the district of Cunningham, North Ayrshire, but its history is not recorded. It can be brown and white or black and white, is very hardy and a good responsive milker.

There are several other dairy breeds, all of which find some place in farming because of their special suitability for particular conditions. The Channel Island cattle give rich creamy milk much in demand for luxury consumption and suitable for butter-making ; the Welsh Black cattle are very hardy and tolerate hill conditions ; the Devons are big, placid creatures entirely fitted for the genial conditions of their native county ; Lincoln has its Reds. The secret of the success of British live-stock farming is that a breed can usually be chosen to suit the conditions and the markets.

Yield is partly a matter of breed and partly also a matter of feeding, and while the dairy farmer likes to choose animals of good yield capacity, he does not normally run them at their highest possible output. The average figure of about 560 gallons is a measure of economical output which the farmer knows he can keep up, and on the basis of which he can sign the contract. Much higher yields can, of course, be obtained if one sets out to get them ; herds averaging 1,000 gallons are no rarity, and 3,000-gallon cows are known. Farmers are sometimes taken to task because they do not work at this more intense pitch. The difference between the very high and the average yield is rather like that between the speed of sixty miles an hour of an occasional car driver and the steady thirty-five miles an hour preferred by the man who has to drive a car all day long and every day.

The health of the cattle affects not only the value of the herd but also the milk. The most important diseases of dairy cattle in this country are tuberculosis, contagious abortion and mastitis. Bovine tuberculosis has been most studied because this form of the disease may also affect human beings. The proportion of infected cows was a few years ago put at 40 per cent. Great efforts, however, are being made to stamp it out. Many valuable cattle have been disposed of because they reacted to the tuberculin test, and the " attested herds scheme " recently introduced has led to notable improvement ; indeed, there was some hope until the war shattered it that tuberculosis might ultimately be eliminated from British herds.

Perhaps the greatest dairy improvement in recent years has been in the production of clean milk. There has been a distinct movement away from cheese- and butter-making on the farm, and instead a demand for cleaner milk

VARIATIONS IN THE NUMBERS OF SHEEP, PIGS AND CATTLE, GREAT BRITAIN 1866-1938

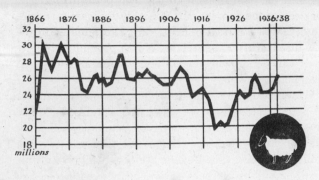

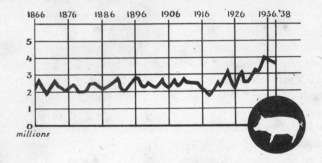

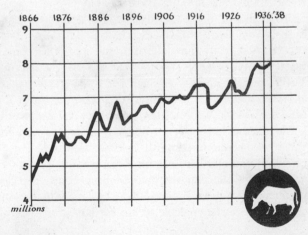

and graded milk. This has led to bacteriological control, and it is now quite usual for even small dairy farmers and workers to know something of the elements of bacteriology and thereby to realise the importance of absolute cleanliness in handling the animals and the need for steam sterilization of all utensils that come in contact with the milk. The National Institute for Research in Dairying, at Shinfield, carries out the basic scientific work, and the Imperial Bureau of Dairy Science collects and distributes relevant information.

Beef production is altogether a separate activity. Dairy farmers, of course, have to produce calves in order to get milk, and about half these, being bull calves, are useless for milk production and therefore sold as beef. Many dairy farmers make no attempt to breed dairy stock, but use a good beef bull and sell all the calves to the beef producer. As their own herd requires replenishing they buy in the market or from a breeder of milking stock.

Much of our beef, however, comes from the special beef breeds, of which some of the best are the beef Shorthorn, much developed in Scotland, the Aberdeen Angus, the Hereford and the Devon. The counties with most beef animals are Devon, which comes easily first ; Northumberland and the West Riding, which come second, followed by Shropshire, the North Riding, Cumberland, Somerset and Leicestershire. The order is thus quite different from that for milk production. Formerly much beef was produced during winter in yards in the Eastern Counties, and large quantities of farmyard manure were made as a valuable by-product ; now there is less, though farmers still do as much as they can. But the greater part of the beef of the country is produced on grassland during summer, using animals brought in either from dairy farms or from the hill country to the West and North, or from Ireland. This was the old Leicestershire and Rutland method, and as it left farmers with much leisure in winter and with unoccupied fields, it was only natural that fox-hunting should have developed there.

SHEEP

Perhaps the greatest change in animal husbandry is that which has come over the sheep. A generation ago large numbers of sheep were born in the hill country to the West and North and sold in autumn to arable farmers in the East and South who, " folded " them on their roots and leys. In addition, the Downland and some of the Marsh farmers bred their own animals, using breeds that had been developed to suit their conditions : Southdowns, Hampshire Downs, Romney Marsh, Suffolk, Lincoln and others. The system had the great advantage of maintaining the fertility of the light, chalky and sandy soils better than any other, and it enriched country life by evolving that unique

THE STABLE INTERIOR
Oil painting by George Morland

A SOW OF THE IMPROVED BREED BELONGING TO HIS GRACE THE DUKE OF BEDFORD

Oil painting by George Morland

THOMAS COKE, M.P. FOR NORFOLK, INSPECTING SOME OF HIS SOUTHDOWN SHEEP
With him, Mr. Walton and the Holkham shepherds
Oil painting by Thomas Weaver

character, the shepherd. It produced during winter and spring-time the quantities of fat mutton needed by the large families of the nineteenth century.

But the costs of root growing steadily rose, good shepherds became scarcer, and increasing quantities of high-quality lamb were coming in from New Zealand (where the Romney Marsh × Southdown cross is very successful) and Australia. Moreover, the public taste was changing; families were smaller, the large fat joint became *démodé*, and instead the demand was for small joints of tender lamb. Farmers met the situation with considerable skill; they turned over to grass-fed sheep and fattened the lambs during summer, selling them at about 40 to 50 lbs. dead weight. As most lambs never see a winter, some characteristics desirable in the old days are unnecessary now, but one thing is essential : the ewes must be prolific and good mothers, they must feed their lambs well. Here the great variety of the British breeds proved an enormous advantage. The Border–Leicester–Cheviot—a magnificent breed that goes back to Robert Bakewell—has satisfied the new conditions. From

25   C

THE WOBURN SHEEPSHEARING
Drawn and engraved by G. Garrard 1811

one hundred ewes it is not difficult to sell one hundred and sixty lambs ; our own flock often gives better results. Most of the ewes have twins and feed them well ; always there are some triplets. It is commonly crossed with Suffolk, Oxford, Southdown or other rams to give lambs suited to various markets.

All the same the passing of the folded sheep is very regrettable. Its place is taken by dairy cattle and grass sheep, one dairy cow being about the equivalent of six to eight sheep. Up till about 1920 the increase in dairy cattle was accompanied by a decrease in the sheep. Since then the position has improved. Dairy cattle still go on increasing, but the sheep no longer decrease ; the total output is therefore increasing.

The ploughing up of grassland since the war has caused farmers to revert to the older method of folding on arable land, but using different crops ; marow-stem kale and sugar-beet tops have in parts of England largely displaced swedes and turnips. J. T. H. Thomas suggests keeping the sheep during winter on arable crops and rough grazing, leaving the better pastures to freshen for the lambs in summer.

PIGS

A whole chapter could be written on pigs, perhaps the most maligned of all farm animals. The pig is naturally clean and intelligent, and no more greedy than any other animal on the farm. There are two types, bacon and pork pigs. The bacon curers require animals of about 180 to 260 lb. live weight, giving dressed carcasses of 135 to 190 lb. The higher weights are preferred in the North Country, and the lower in the South. Animals should be ready when about seven or eight months old. Porkers, on the other hand, should be lighter, about 120 to 130 lb. weight—*i.e.*, 100 lb. carcass—and should be ready at five or five-and-a-half months. The difference is partly in breed, partly in management. Large Whites—evolved largely by Yorkshire weavers —and Tamworths make good bacon ; Middle White and Berkshires make excellent pork, while the Blacks and Saddlebacks can make either. Well-chosen crosses are, however, commonly used. Successful pig-keeping is a very skilful business, and there is a vast difference in results produced by a first-class and a poor pigman.

Farmers have formed pig recording societies, the officer of which visits farms to record the performance of all the pigs. The litters are counted, the young pigs weighed at definite intervals so that their growth rates can be determined. Note is taken of the weight and quality of the carcass at the bacon factory. Unthrifty sows and boars can thus be eliminated and more effective ones used for breeding ; the rations also can be fully controlled.

27

Pigs can make better use of food than any other farm animal, and under suitable conditions 1 lb. of carcass can be obtained from about 5 lb. of dry food as compared with about 16 lb. needed by sheep, and 22 lb. by beef cattle. But proper feeding is essential, and much work has been done on this subject. The ration must be fully adequate in mineral matter and in protein ; it is often necessary to supplement these by additions of mineral salts and of meat or fish meal. Proper housing is essential. Pigs do well in the open air and can produce litters there, though they need huts for night shelter ; but for fattening they must be brought into proper sties, which must be warm and properly ventilated and, above all, clean. Many efforts have been made to work out economic and effective designs for pig-houses, and some very good ones can be seen on our farms, but there are also some very bad ones.

III

THE ARABLE FARMING OF ENGLAND

ARABLE farming is practicable only within certain limits of rainfall ; usually (but with exceptions determined by other conditions) between about 15 and 35 inches annually. None of Great Britain has as little as 15 inches, but much of it has more than 35 inches. Arable farming is mostly practised in the regions with less than 30 inches of rain, *i.e.*, east of a line drawn from Berwick-on-Tweed to the Isle of Wight.

The best way to see English arable farming is to travel along the Great North road, making many detours to the east so as to visit the seed-growing and dairy regions of Essex ; the pleasing villages of Suffolk, famous for its beautiful sheep, cattle and horses ; and the grain and sugar-beet regions of

A FARMYARD, NEAR PRINCES RISBOROUGH, BUCKINGHAMSHIRE
Water colour by Samuel Palmer

Norfolk, which has always been a region of agricultural improvement. Then comes the country round the Wash, the highly fertile Fen country, thickly set with wheat, sugar-beet, potatoes and other less common crops like mustard and celery. Next should be visited the part of Lincolnshire appropriately called Holland, and reminiscent of the wide, flat expanses of its namesake, where the land merges into the sky and the rivers have to be dyked to keep them within bounds. Here is some of the richest and best farmed land in the country. First one passes through the Spalding area of fertile silt, where heavy crops of sugar-beet are grown ; then to Holbeach, the centre of potato culture, with favoured regions like the land around Freiston, that will carry two crops a year—early potatoes followed by sprouts or broccoli. Further north comes the higher land of Lincolnshire, the Heath and the Wolds, with much grain, sugar-beet and general farming. Then, crossing the Humber, we enter the rich vale of York with its adaptable family farmers, who find potatoes better than sugar-beet ; to the east lie the Wolds with their large farms, big arable fields, and great stretches of corn and turnips. Northwards again we get into

29

Durham, famous as the home of the Shorthorns, once a beautiful county till the mining villages disfigured it ; but on its coastal strip some good agriculture is still practised. Then to Northumberland, where in the lower country, especially along Tweedside, there are some famous farms. Then it is imperative to move into the Lothians to see some of the magnificent farming around Dunbar and along the Forth, and still further north to the beef districts of Aberdeen. For every crop a fascinating story could be told, but we can only briefly refer to one, the potato crop in Lincolnshire, now one of the most important branches of agriculture in the country.

The chief potato-growing region in England is the Holland division of Lincolnshire, which can be visited from the comfortable little town of Holbeach. Here, more than 30 per cent. of the arable land is in potatoes.

The enterprise was started about 1880 by James Thompson, a bankrupt farmer, of South Lincolnshire, who had turned potato buyer, and William Dennis, of Kirton, till then a waggoner. Some potatoes were already grown, but yields were low, cultivation was poor, and little manure was given— a story long survived of a farmer boasting because he used 2 cwt. of " artificials." per acre. Both men realised that the newly-introduced Magnum Bonum should do well. Thompson tried it and failed ; he tried a second time and failed again, but at the third attempt he succeeded. Then came Up-to-Date and the recognition that it would yield large crops if heavily manured and well cultivated ; this made the success complete. Finally the seed was " boxed " or sprouted before planting, which increased the yield and hastened the harvest and made the whole enterprise safer and more profitable. This method was discovered by a Kirton gardener who by accident had left some potatoes in a basket through the winter ; they grew nice sprouts and when planted gave larger and better plants than usual.

Later developments were not always smooth ; there have, indeed, been days of tense excitement, as when a new local variety, El Dorado, captured the public fancy, so that its seed mounted daily in price and finally sold for more than its weight in gold. Episodes like that, however, do not really help agriculture.

Potato growing in Lincolnshire has now become a great art in which the growers take much pride. Varieties are sown in sequence to spread the lifting and delivery season ; great discretion is shown in choosing sorts that suit the conditions and the market, and setting each in its most appropriate field. Large dressings of manure are given, and the cultivation is beyond reproach ; in a bad season the growers may lose money " in hatfuls," as one of them put it, but in a good season all comes right again. Yields of 10 or 12 tons of saleable potatoes are not uncommon ; the average for the country is 7 tons.

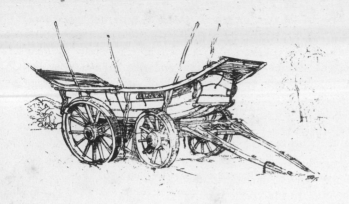

THREE TYPES OF ENGLISH FARM CARTS

1. A Hereford Waggon (Mathon, near Malvern).   2. A Kent Waggon (Meopham)
3. A Gloucestershire " hoop-raved " Waggon (West Littleton).
Drawings by T. Hennell from *Change in the Farm*, by T. Hennell

In certain other regions the proportion of arable land under potatoes is also high. In the Isle of Ely the percentage is nearly 25 ; in Lancaster 20 (this clusters mostly round Ormskirk). Then follow Cheshire with 12 ; Bedford, Durham, Stafford and the West Riding, each with about 10 per cent. There are considerable areas also in Lindsey, Norfolk, Essex and Devon.

The Manuring of Crops

The farmers of Great Britain use considerable quantities of manure, both animal and artificial, to increase their crops. Much of this comes from the feeding-stuffs imported for our large animal population, from which considerable amounts of nitrogen, potash and phosphate pass into the farmyard manure. It is estimated that the farmers of Great Britain make some 15 to 20 million tons of farmyard manure annually for use on their 30 million acres of cultivated land. In addition, large and increasing amounts of artificial fertilizers are used. Separate figures are not available for the different regions, but for the whole of the British Islands, including Eire, on 44 million acres of cultivated land the quantities of plant food used were, before the war upset things :—

	Nitrogen (N) Thousand Tons	Phosphoric Acid (P_2O_5) Thousand Tons	Potash (K_2O) Thousand Tons
As artificial fertilizers and " organics "	80	190	80
As farmyard manure (approximate only) ...	120	50	160
Total ...	200	240	240

Artificial fertilizers were first made at Rothamsted by John Bennett Lawes, and the Rothamsted experiments continue to furnish some of the best information about them. Manurial schemes have been worked out for different parts of the country based on crop requirements and soil deficiencies, and official advisers help farmers by field experiments and analyses to make the best use of fertilizers. Recently also the importance of the " trace " elements, boron, manganese, iron, copper, cobalt and others, has been recognised, and farmers can be advised when they are needed, and in what quantities.

Sufficiency of lime is essential for the proper action of fertilizers and manures, and free analyses of soils are made by the advisory officers and advice given as to the amount needed.

Crop Improvement

The use of proper varieties is absolutely essential to the success of arable farming. Great improvements in English crops have taken place. Until

MR. PAWLETT WITH HIS LEICESTER SHEEP, WINNERS AT THE FIRST ROYAL SHOW, 1839
Oil painting by an unknown artist

HARVEST FIELDS

The Village of Stanton Harcourt in the background

Water colour by William Turner of Oxford

SEED TIME
Water colour by J. F. Herring, 1856

recent years they were largely due to observant countrymen, and most were accidental, but more systematic methods are now used.

Cereals.—One of the most useful varieties of barley ever grown in this country was called Chevallier ; it was discovered about 1820 by the oddest chance. A labourer, John Andrews, of Debenham, Suffolk, was walking home after threshing out some barley, and was annoyed by part of an ear that had got into his shoe and hurt his foot. When he got home he took off his shoe and shook it out ; he then noticed that it was better and more shapely than usual, so he kept it, and at the proper time sowed the grain in his garden. The plants grew well and produced grains like the parent. Again he saved these seeds and grew the plants, and this time, of course, there were a number of them. The local clergyman and landowner, the Rev. John Chevallier, now intervened, took the seed and grew it in his field. It still retained its superior character, and was seen and admired by farmers, who secured small amounts of the seed and multiplied and distributed it till finally the barley was very widely grown. It was named not after the labourer, as this century would require, but after the clergyman.

Accidents like this gave us some of our best varieties of farm crops.

New varieties began to multiply when cross-breeding was taken up by growers. Plumage-Archer, now our commonest sort of barley, was raised by E. S. Beaven by crossing two older sorts, Plumage and Archer.

33   D

It is unsafe to count on a succession of gifted craftsmen to produce the new sorts as needed; nor is it necessary. The modern science of genetics enables a plant breeder to some extent to build up a plant according to a specification, and already this work has begun.

The most marked success has been obtained in wheat breeding; the chief aims have been to combine high yield with certain other characters, such as strong straw, resistance to disease, especially the terrible "rust," high baking quality, suitability for certain conditions, etc. In Great Britain the best known examples are Sir Rowland Biffen's Little Joss and Yeoman, the first for light or poor soils, the second for more fertile conditions. One of the best known cereal-breeding stations in the world is at Svalof, Sweden, but Holland and France have also produced good varieties that do well in this country. These are tested by the National Institute of Agricultural Botany under a variety of different conditions, and recommendations are published.

On soils of medium fertility the most suitable wheats are the white soft varieties, Wilhelmina, produced in Holland by L. Brockema crossing Squarehead with a Dutch wheat, Zeeuwsche; Wilma, a selection from it; and Victor, a very similar English wheat. If the soil is light, however, the rainfall should be not less than about 25 inches a year. On soils of medium texture the Square Heads Master group, Red Standard, and other selections are very good. These various wheats are perhaps more widely grown than any others in England. On more fertile heavy soils Yeoman is very successful and is widely grown; the Swedish wheats, Iron, Steel, Weibull's Standard, etc., also do well, and can indeed be sown also on medium and light soils; they are not as popular as Yeoman. On poor heavy soils the old Rivet grows well, and on poor light ones, Little Joss. All these varieties are suitable for insular climatic conditions; they are less useful on the great continental plains, just as the prairie successes, Marquis and others, cannot profitably be grown here.

Potatoes.—Enormous numbers of varieties of potatoes have been bred, and occasionally one is a marked improvement on those in use. Some men have a special flair for this work and are really great craftsmen. James Clarke, of Christchurch, Hampshire, produced Magnum Bonum, which Messrs. Sutton put on the market in 1876, and which opened the way for the modern potato-growing industry, but he left no record of how he did it. Archibald Findlay, of Auchtermuchty, raised, among others, Up-to-Date, for some time the most popular potato in the country, and Majestic, at present one of the most widely-grown sorts, but is silent about their origin. King Edward, its chief competitor for the first place, was raised by an unknown Northumberland gardener and saved almost by accident; its ancestry is unknown.

A variety usually lasts only about twenty-five years; it then begins to degenerate. This was formerly attributed to the circumstance that the reproduction is vegetative and assexual; it is more probably due to disease.

The chief problems at present confronting the potato breeder are those of disease. The potato blight that ruined the Irish crop for several successive years in the 1840's, and so caused the terrible Irish famine, was imported from America in the increasing traffic that followed the displacement of sailing ships by steamers.

A cure was found by accident. A Bordeaux grape grower, worried by the depredations of mischievous boys, conceived the idea of spraying his grapes with the disgusting looking mess that results from adding lime water to a solution of copper sulphate. The mixture not only kept off the boys, but also the destructive mildew, and, as scientists had shown that the blight was also due to a fungus, the spray was tried on potatoes and found to be a satisfactory protective.

A new trouble arose about 1905, when the wart disease came in, also from America. This is a soil-borne fungus and attacks the tuber; it is very difficult to cope with, and no cure has yet been found. Fortunately G. C. Gough, an inspector of the Ministry of Agriculture, heard on his rounds of occasional sorts of potatoes standing up healthy in fields of diseased potatoes, and recognised them as immune. He thus started the search for immune varieties, which has been very successful. Majestic, Great Scot, Doon Star, Golden Wonder and others are immune; on the other hand, King Edward, Up-to-Date, Eclipse Epicure and other popular varieties are not, and have to be kept to soils free from wart disease.

Much more serious are the virus diseases, to which no variety is immune, though some, *e.g.*, Epicure, King Edward and Great Scot, are somewhat resistant either to leaf roll or mosaic, or both. The difficulty is that these diseases are carried by certain aphids and get into the " seed " (*i.e.*, the tubers), so affecting the next generation. No cure is known and the losses are considerable.

The only safe plan is to avoid them by using healthy seed. Fortunately, some parts of the country, notably in Scotland, are not very suitable for the aphids that transmit the diseases, and in consequence their potatoes are or can be free from them; seed from these regions has therefore a special value.

The Scottish Department of Agriculture has a very efficient inspection scheme, and its certificates are everywhere accepted. Meanwhile investigations on virus diseases are made at a number of stations : at Cambridge, Rothamsted and elsewhere.

Sugar-beet is an entirely modern introduction. Thirty years ago practically none was grown, though indefatigable workers, including Earl Denbigh, Sir Beville Stanier, Sir Alfred Wood and others, were urging its cultivation, and a few experiments had been made to show that this was possible. Two factors finally compelled agriculturists to grow it. Swedes and turnips were proving more and more uneconomical ; some alternative food was necessary on arable land for the sheep, and sugar-beet tops proved to be very effective. The Government was beginning to realise the danger of being wholly dependent on overseas countries for sugar, and decided that a substantial part of the United Kingdom's annual consumption of over two million tons should be grown here.

The first modern factory was built in 1912 at Cantley, Norfolk. By 1922 the area of sugar-beet in England and Wales was 8,400 acres, and it rose steeply till in 1934 it exceeded 396,000 acres, with an area of about 7,500 acres in Scotland. But this proved rather too much, and the acreage fell somewhat till the war made further sugar production very desirable.

In the early years Dutch and Czechoslovakian experts gave considerable help, but English experts and farmers soon got down to the problems arising out of our special conditions, and a network of research and advisory services was set up by the sugar factories and is now taken over by the Sugar Commission.

The yield for the ten years 1929–38 averaged 8·6 tons per acre, but it varies with the season, and ranged from 6·6 in 1938 to 10·2 tons per acre in 1934. All the seed had in the first instance to come from the Continent, but home supplies are now being organised. Diseases and pests are closely watched and manurial and cultivation problems are studied ; sugar-beet is perhaps more fully investigated than any other crop.

IV

IMPROVEMENT OF THE GRASSLAND

THE central and western parts of England, with their mild, moist climate and wide expanse of clay vales, are eminently suited to grass, and some of the most fertile of our pastures are found there. It is not uncommon for a Leicestershire pasture to fatten one bullock per acre during the growing season without additional food ; the live weight increases may be 3 or 4 lb. per head per day. In low-lying regions all round the coast there are some excellent pastures, *e.g.*, Romney Marsh in Kent, and Pawlett Hams in Somerset. At the other end of the scale is the so-called rough grazing—poor, almost worthless grass, or even heather ; and in between come all shades of goodness and badness. No crop varies so much in value as grass.

Over most parts of Great Britain grass grows so easily that farmers have to spend considerable time and trouble in keeping it out of their arable crops. It is therefore the easiest and cheapest of all crops to grow. It is, however, not a single species, but a mixture of many plants of very unequal value. The poorer the land the larger the number of species as a rule, because nothing grows vigorously enough to crowd out the seedlings that arise from chance seeds blown in, and the different species settle down to some kind of equilibrium. Directly, however, human or animal intervention arises this equilibrium is disturbed ; whatever is done favours some species more than others, and these grow, crowding out their less fortunate neighbours. The art of managing grassland consists in manipulating this very mixed flora so as to encourage the useful plants and suppress the others. On the Rothamsted grass plots the poor unmanured land has some fifty different species, while the rich well-treated flora has only about ten to twenty.

For grazing purposes the most useful are wild white clover and rye grass, and the problem is to develop them.

In 1896, Somerville showed that dressings of basic slag greatly increased the growth of white clover, and in consequence improved the feeding value of the herbage. The following live-weight increases were obtained with grazing sheep on poor pasture at Cockle Park, Northumberland :—

No Manure	Basic Slag	Increase due to Slag
37	117	80 lb. per acre

British farmers now use some 300,000 tons of basic slag annually.

Excess of soil moisture is harmful and must be remedied by drainage. This may be a major regional operation. Frequently, however, it is only a matter of individual fields. For this purpose mole draining has been developed, and where practicable it is both cheap and efficient. The drain is cut by a plough consisting of a steel cylinder with a pointed end carried on a strong steel framework and dragged through the soil by a tractor so as to make a tunnel 2 or 3 inches in diameter and 18 inches to 2½ feet below the surface. The tunnel is not unlike that made by a mole ; hence the name. It is far more permanent than one might think, and provided its outfall into the ditch is piped and bricked it functions for fifteen or twenty years or more. The work is done by contract by the large ploughing organisations.

While grass can do without cultivation, it grows much better if its roots are periodically aerated and if at the proper time it is rolled. The two operations are to some extent mutually contradictory, and the farmer's skill consists in knowing just when to perform them and how far to go. Harrows made of strong spikes mounted on a heavy frame, or of knives fixed on a rotating bar, are dragged over the turf, cutting narrow gashes down which air can penetrate. The grass looks ruined, but it soon starts into vigorous growth and becomes much better than ever before.

Only young grass is very palatable or nutritious ; it must never be allowed to grow old. Perennial youth can be assured by preventing the formation of seed, which is the natural end of the plant's life ; if the flowering heads are not eaten by the animals, they must be cut by the mowing machine.

Manuring and grazing are among the chief methods of grassland management. Basic slag favours clover ; nitrogenous manures favour deep-rooting vegetation unless the soil is very acid, when fescues and other shallow-rooted plants predominate. Drainage favours deep-rooting grasses. Grazing is more complex in its effects. Resting the grass during winter and spring allows the rye grass to grow ; this checks other grasses, weeds and clover, and dominates the summer flora. Thus are produced the grassy Midland pastures. Heavy grazing in spring, on the other hand, keeps down the grasses and allows the clover to become dominant, but overgrazing in winter and spring and undergrazing in summer and autumn— unfortunately a common method of mismanagement—allows weeds to develop, especially thistles, bent and Yorkshire fog.

Sheep and cattle graze differently ; sheep nibble with their teeth, and therefore prefer short vegetation, leaving the taller growth untouched, while cattle put their tongues round the vegetation to bring it into their mouths ; hence they prefer the taller growing plants. Sheep and cattle together therefore make better use of grassland than either separately. The best farmers graze a field intensively for a short time, say, ten or twenty days ; then rest it completely until the grass has grown again, which may be another two or three weeks ; then graze again. This rotational grazing combined with heavy manuring gave remarkable results in the experiments at Jealott's Hill. As for other intensive methods, however, wide adoption is possible only under suitable economic conditions.

Much more drastic methods have been successfully used by Sir George Stapledon in the hill country of Wales and the Welsh marches. At the higher altitude (up to 1,400 feet) much of the herbage consists of *Molinia*, *Nardus*, bent grass, etc., which are almost worthless as animal food. The first step in improving a Molinia pasture is to fence and instal watering facilities, then to mow and burn the roughage, apply lime, phosphate, nitro-chalk and hard grazing. After four or five years an Agrostis pasture develops. This can now be ploughed or " roughed up," dressed with lime and basic slag, and sown with a mixture of leafy perennial rye grass and wild white clover. These are the basis of all mixtures. Cocksfoot can be added on the stronger soils, crested dogs-tail on thin dry soils, red fescue on poor soils; these two and rough-stalked meadow grass compete successfully with weeds and keep them out. Plantain, hawkweed, catsear, daisy, etc., are useful as collectors of mineral matter, such as lime and phosphate, from the soil. Herbage which in summer carried only one ewe and one store lamb per acre, and fattened neither, has been transformed to carry four ewes and four lambs per acre, fattening about 60 per cent. of the lambs. In winter the original herbage carried no more than one ewe to four acres, while two ewes per acre can be carried by the new herbage.

This ploughing-up of hill pasture became practicable with the advent of the caterpillar tractor and the rotary cultivators driven by power take-off from the tractor. These methods have been successfully used for improving many poor lowland pastures.

There has been much improvement of hill grazing in Scotland; the essential features are the controlled burning of heather pastures, cultivation of Nardus-Molinia pastures with disc harrows to encourage Agrostis and Yorkshire fog, dressings of phosphate and use of renovating mixtures.

TEMPORARY LEYS AND LONG LEYS

However well permanent grass is managed, it does not give as good yields as temporary grass, the so-called ley or " seeds mixture," sown as one of the courses in the rotation of arable crops. There are several reasons for this. The temporary ley benefits by the good fertility conditions developed during the rotation; the seed is good and of well-chosen varieties; the crop is not allowed to remain long enough to suffer serious competition from weeds. Further, it is free from the parasitic worms, etc., that tend to accumulate in permanent pasture and cause much disease, especially to young animals. Against the temporary ley, however, is the very serious difficulty that in the eastern part of England it is liable to fail because of spring droughts, so leaving the farmer short on food for his animals. Further, wild white clover only slowly establishes itself and gives little produce during its first year. The grasses also may only slowly develop. The most usual plant for a one-year ley is red clover ; this grows rapidly and produces a considerable weight of herbage in its first year. Unfortunately it is not permanent and does not usually survive a second winter, at any rate in the eastern part of England ; further, it is rather liable to soil-borne diseases and is best grown only about once in eight years on any particular field.

In other parts of England where spring droughts are less frequent and winters are milder a temporary ley can persist for several years. The mixture includes red and other clovers, perennial and Italian rye grass (*Lolium perenne* and *L. italicum*) ; the latter has the advantage that it will grow throughout a mild winter and provide animal food early in spring, while the perennial is slower in starting, though it does much better in the end. Cocksfoot (*Dactylis glomerata*) also provides early food, but it becomes coarse later on. Timothy, much grown in the United States, is not very useful in British conditions. The wider adoption of long leys in place of some of the permanent grass would greatly increase the output from British farmers.

GRASS CONSERVATION

While grass is one of the best and cheapest foods for animals, it is unreliable. Growing grass is very susceptible to weather conditions ; it is at its best only for a short time, and throughout the winter it provides nothing. Winter food has therefore always been a difficulty. The common procedure is to close some fields during spring and summer and allow the grass to complete its growth, then to make it into hay ; this can be kept not only for the succeeding winter, but if necessary for two or even three years, and it gives excellent food for the animals. In the old days hay-making required a great deal of labour, but it had some of the elements of a picnic ; nowadays machinery has been devised for making, collecting and baling it ; the cost therefore remains low.

In wet weather, however, hay-making is difficult. Northern farmers have devised ways of overcoming the trouble, but these have not spread much in the south. An alternative used in a series of wet summers is to convert the grass into silage. This involves considerable wastage, but it answers, and the newer methods are considerably more economical than the old. Large wooden or concrete silos are an advantage but not a necessity, and stout paper can now be used, kept in position by wire netting.

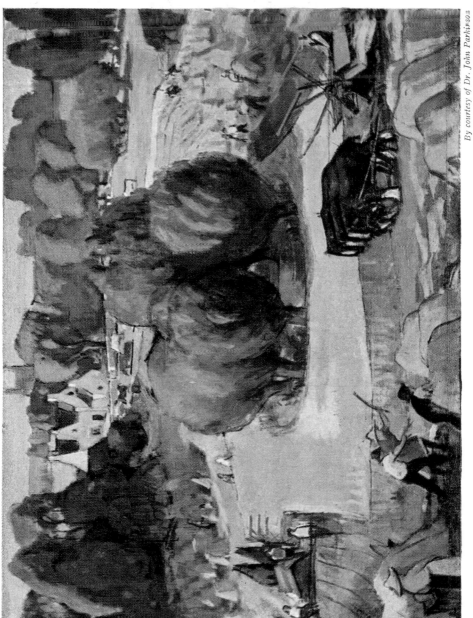

THE HARVEST

Oil painting by James Bateman

THE BLACK SOW   THE RED OX

Tempera paintings by John Armstrong

By courtesy of the Artist and of the Leicester Galleries, London

More recently machines have been introduced for drying the grass by heat, and these allow the young grass to be conserved. The resulting product is much more nutritious per ton than hay, and is indeed comparable with concentrated feeding-stuffs in food value. The plant is expensive and the process is rather outside the ordinary range of farm experience, so it is not adopted widely, but it opens up considerable possibilities.

In mild regions certain grasses, especially Italian rye grass and timothy, continue to grow during winter, and Stapledon has selected specially vigorous strains which afford a certain amount of keep during the difficult months December to March.

THE PLOUGHING-UP CAMPAIGN

During the first year of war over two million acres of grassland were ploughed up and put into arable crops. This is often regarded as a clear gain ; actually some protein food is lost by the change. N. C. Wright makes a provisional balance sheet for the United Kingdom as follows :—

Gains and Losses from Ploughing-up Grassland, United Kingdom
(N. C. Wright)

	Protein Equivalent Thousand Tons		Starch Equivalent Thousand Tons	
(a) Nutrients produced on newly-ploughed acreage (2,034,000 acres) :				
Cereals, including straw	110		1,030	
Potatoes	10		195	
Fodder crops	25		215	
		145		1,440
(b) Nutrients lost from ploughing-up of grassland :				
Rotation grassland	95		450	
Permanent grassland	110		705	
		205		1,155
Net change		− 60		+ 285

The justification for the ploughing-up policy is not only the increase in food units, but the change in the kind of food. Cereals and potatoes are human food ; grass is not, but must be converted by the animal, and the process is not economical. At least 5 lb. of feeding-stuffs are necessary to produce 1 lb. of edible animal products. The real gain therefore is that this wasteful conversion is eliminated. Even for the animal there is an advantage : the loss of protein equivalent through ploughing-up is in summer, when there is more

E

HARVEST: A VIEW IN HEREFORDSHIRE
Oil painting by G. R. Lewis

grass than can be used economically ; in winter there is an actual gain. It is a great tribute to the skill and resourcefulness of British farmers that they have adapted their feeding systems to the new conditions. In spite of war-time difficulties the numbers of cattle and of sheep are well maintained.

V

AGRICULTURE'S CONTRIBUTION TO THE NATIONAL WELL-BEING

WHAT does British agriculture contribute to the national well-being, and what do the farmers and farm workers get out of it ? In order to appreciate fully the answer to these questions it must be recognised that British farmers have had to meet two great difficulties from which many of the Continental farmers have been free. The first is that until recently our farmers have never known when they could sell their produce, or what price they would obtain for it. In consequence they were never able to do all they would have liked because of the fear that the price might be un-remunerative. The selling, too, was almost entirely an individual matter, and at least one day a week was spent at the market, often without much recompense. Secondly, the road off the farm has always been very easy for the young people, and in consequence farmers have had to pay wages sufficient to keep the necessary men on the land, whether prices were good or bad.

The first of these difficulties is being met by a more organised relation between the farmer and the buyers ; a contract system has been developed for milk, sugar-beet and wheat, and organised marketing arrangements for potatoes and live-stock ; these are in the hands of marketing boards. The wages difficulty has been met by increasing the efficiency of the labour units, partly by raising the standard of education, partly by the use of more machinery, but chiefly by modifying the system of farming so as to allow greater economy of labour.

Broadly speaking, about 900,000 persons were regularly employed in agriculture in England and Wales in 1937–38, of whom about 300,000 were farmers or relations assisting, and some 600,000 were paid workers. The number of farmers remains fairly steady, but the number of workers is falling ; in 1930 they had exceeded 700,000, and in 1925 over 800,000. But in spite of this fall in number the value of the output has been about £200,000,000, i.e., more than £200 per head, and this value is rising even after correction is made for changes in price level. The 900,000 of 1937–38 actually produced more food than the 1,100,000 of 1925. This increase in efficiency of the labour unit has been marked and continuous.

43

The British farm worker (including the farmer) turns out considerably more food per annum than any on the Continent. The figures are so striking that they must be quoted :—

Value of Agricultural Output in Great Britain, Germany and Western European Countries, 1937 (P. Lamartine Yates)

		Output per Worker, £		Wages per Hired Worker, Shillings Weekly	Acres per Worker	Live-stock Units per Worker	Output per Acre, £	
		Gross	Net				Gross	Net
Great Britain	...	240	200	30–36	33·8	10·3	7	6
Denmark	...	180	155	23–26	15·7	8·4	11	10
Netherlands	...	150	120	23–30	9·0	4·9	17	14
Belgium	...	110	100	18–22	7·4	3·4	15	14
Switzerland	...	110	100	27–29	7·1	4·3	17	15
France	...	90	90	20–28	11·6	2·8	8	8
Germany	...	70	70	18–23	7·9	2·8	8	8

The money value of the output per worker in Great Britain is three times that in Germany, double that in France, Switzerland and Belgium, and 30 per cent. above that in Denmark. Much of the difference lies in the systems of farming. Live-stock play a more important part in British agriculture than on the Continent, and they give a higher money return for the labour expended on them than do ordinary agricultural crops ; indeed, the output per worker is closely related to the number of live-stock units per worker. Live-stock represent nearly 70 per cent. of the total value of the agricultural output of England and Wales, and over 80 per cent. of that of Scotland. These figures are average for the country ; in the arable regions the proportion is lower, *e.g.* in the Eastern Counties in 1938 live-stock and dairy produce represented 58 per cent. of the output. But in the grass regions of the West and North nearly all the output is live-stock.

Milk is the chief of the live-stock products, and its value is rising ; cattle come next, then pigs and sheep. The output of eggs is considerable and is equal in value to that of mutton and lamb, and far ahead of that of wheat :—

	Milk and Dairy Produce	Cattle	Pigs	Sheep and Lambs	Eggs	Poultry	Wool	Total
Million £ (average 1930 to 1937–38), England & Wales	53·1	26·5	21·2	15·4	15·7	5·7	1·8	139·4

The crops sold off the farm are much less in value :—

	Wheat	All Corn	Potatoes	Sugar-beet	Other Crops	All Crops
Million £ (average 1930–31 to 1937–38), England and Wales	4·6	10·7	12·1	5·4	5·5	33·7

44

These, however, represent only part of the total crops grown; the large amount fed to animals is put to their account; it represents some 80 per cent. of their food. The full data show certain well-marked trends: an increased production of milk, pigs, vegetables and wheat.

WHAT AGRICULTURE PROVIDES FOR THE CONSUMER

Our farmers and farm workers produced before the war about 40 per cent. of the value of the food consumed in this country; one farm labour unit therefore " fed " seventeen persons. This is a better performance than in any other European country. The Germans " fed " only seven persons, and on a lower level. But the 40 per cent. home production is not evenly distributed over the various foods; the proportions were in 1937–38 approximately :—

Milk and Potatoes	Vegetables Per Cent.	Meat Per Cent.	Wheat, Cheese Per Cent.	Butter Per Cent.
Practically all	70–80	50	20	10

The low production of butter and of cheese is due to the fact that about $2\frac{1}{2}$ to 3 gallons of milk are needed to make 1 lb. of butter, and about 1 gallon to make 1 lb. of cheese, and the farmer can obtain a higher price by selling milk as liquid than if he converts it into one of these products.

WHAT THE COUNTRYMAN GETS OUT OF IT

The farm worker's minimum wage is fixed by the Wages Board; it rose steadily to 35/- per week in 1939, and in July, 1940, was raised to 48/-. The actual wage is higher; the horsemen, cowmen, pigmen, shepherds, tractor drivers and other skilled workers receive higher rates, and those normally on the minimum rate obtain extra pay during hay-time and harvest. On our own farm at Rothamsted only two out of the ten regular workers are on the minimum rate, and their additional payment averages 2/- per week. Cottages are usually provided and the standard rent is 3/- per week, though higher rents can now be charged if the Wages Board approve. Some of the skilled men who must live on the farm because of the animals have their cottages rent free; four out of our ten do so. In addition, adequate garden facilities are provided, and on most farms something in kind is usually given, e.g., milk and potatoes at wholesale rates, wood logs for burning whenever available, etc. It is difficult to assess the value of all these " extras," but over the year they are substantial. Then, too, there is no loss due to short period stoppages; even time lost in sickness is often paid for, and there is no fear of unemployment for a good man. It is much more difficult to say what income farmers make. Most farmers judge their financial position by their bank balance, and over a run of years this affords a rough-and-ready guide. But even if all financial transactions passed through the bank this would still furnish only a receipts and payments account, not the income and expenditure account which is the one really wanted. The main trouble arises from the difficulty of allowing for the improvement or deterioration during the year in land, live-stock and implements. By making certain assumptions and keeping to them for a period of years a defensible estimate of income can be drawn up, but the process is by no means easy. Farmers are encouraged to keep costing accounts so that they may know the profitableness or otherwise of their various activities, but to arrive at their true income is for many of them so difficult that the Inland Revenue authorities allow most of them to be assessed for income tax on the basis of their rental. These uncertainties do not deter men from entering the profession ; a farmer's son frequently succeeds him on the same farm, and satisfactory farms are usually in good demand if they should fall vacant.

The landowners have suffered most severely from the changes since the last war. Many sold their land to the farmers, who thereupon had to undertake both landowner and farmer responsibilities ; this proved very difficult and sometimes impossible. High taxation and heavy death duties have caused indefinite postponement of desirable developments, though in some cases, for example, housing and drainage, the situation has been eased by public grants. The loss of leadership and of landowners' capital has created difficulties. We are still confronted with the problem of finding a way up for the young man of ability but no money.

WHAT OF THE FUTURE ?

British agriculture has always suffered from the fact that the community has never for long decided what part it should play in the national life. During war-time its importance is universally recognised, but in peace-time there is less interest and little agreement ; some advocate a flourishing agriculture producing as much as possible of all essential foodstuffs, while others consider that we should import a large part of our foods so as to foster an export of manufactured goods and restrict our own agriculture to the production of higher qualities of food ; making it, in fact, somewhat of a luxury trade. Either kind of agriculture could be developed quite well, but in absence of any decision the farmer is left in a great state of uncertainty.

Assuming the community decides that British agriculture shall continue after the war as during the war to make its maximum contribution to national food production, it will become imperative to remove the uncertainties of price

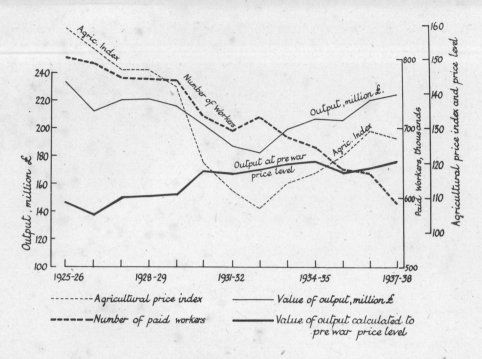

Agricultural price index --------
Number of paid workers -------
Value of output, million £ ———
Value of output calculated to pre war price level ———

that in recent years have played such havoc with our farming. Every other large industry works on contracts of one sort or another ; agriculture in the past has been an exception. The success of the sugar-beet and milk contracts shows that the system can work also in agriculture, and it should be extended to other farm products. But contracts imply a carefully considered compromise between importation and home production, and, above all, a decision which only the Government can give : what proportion of our various foodstuffs should be produced at home ?

Once this great uncertainty about prices is overcome the way is open for the farmer to improve his methods so as to raise his output per acre without, however, lowering the output per man. Improvements must constantly be sought in the system and in its details ; in particular, the system must be closely adapted to the natural conditions of the farm ; the fertility of the soil must be maintained and, if possible, enhanced by proper management and proper manuring ; the quality of the live-stock must be improved, and watch must be kept for better varieties of crops. But, above all, the efficiency of the farmer and farm-worker must continuously be increased ; research and education must go hand-in-hand, gaining new knowledge and spreading it broadcast.

The financial rewards of agriculture are never great, but the life is full of the interest that comes of dealing with living things and spending one's days in the open air, watching the growing crops and tending the animals that furnish food for the nation. It is likely, therefore, that the community will realise that the life offered to a man by agriculture is better than that offered by industry or commerce by all kinds of imponderables which make for what we may sum up as " quality." There is thus no reason to be pessimistic about the future of English farming.